JAN'S ATOMIC HEART

АТОМНОЕ СЕРДЦЕ ЯНА

BY SIMON ROY

new reliable press

www.newreliable.com

JAN'S ATOMIC HEART June 2009

Published by New Reliable Press, 313-3142 St. Johns St., Port Moody, BC, Canada, V3H 5E5

10 9 8 7 6 5 4 3 2 1

Printed in Canada. June 2009.

ISBN: 978-0-9738079-5-0

www.newreliable.com

FRANKFURT.
SOMETIME IN THE FAR-ISH FUTURE.

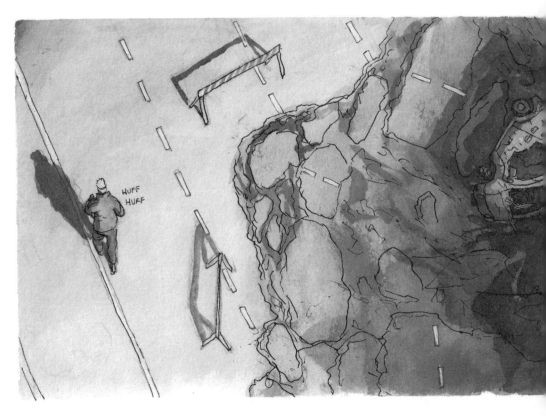

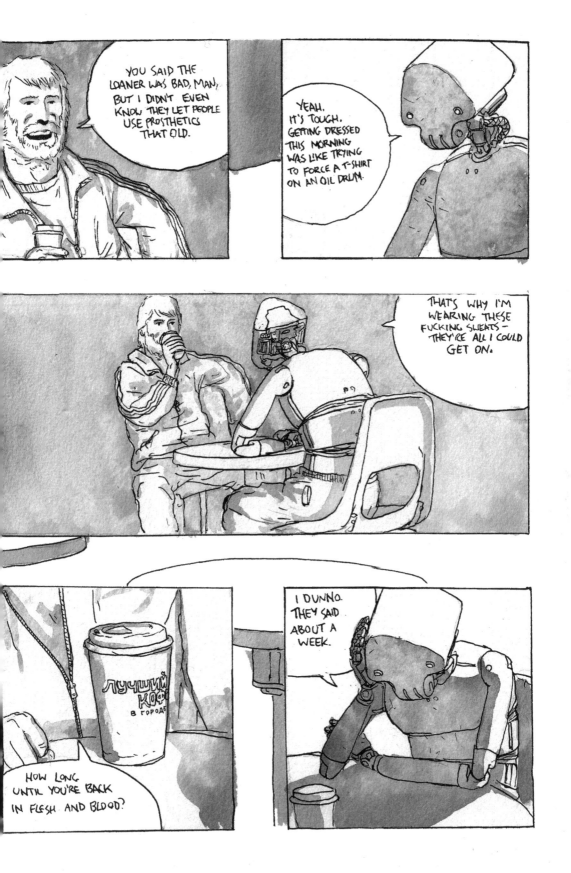

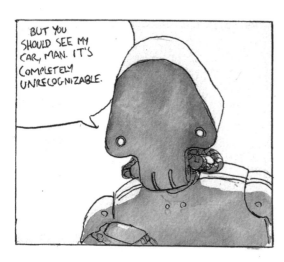

BUT YOU SHOULD SEE MY CAR, MAN. IT'S COMPLETELY UNRECOGNIZABLE.

I CAN IMAGINE. I DON'T KNOW MANY PEOPLE WHO'VE BEEN HIT BY A TRAIN.

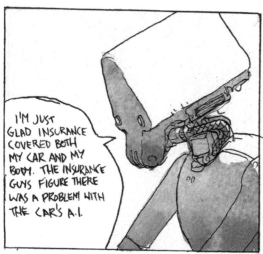

I'M JUST GLAD INSURANCE COVERED BOTH MY CAR AND MY BODY. THE INSURANCE GUYS FIGURE THERE WAS A PROBLEM WITH THE CAR'S A.I.

MANUFACTURER ERROR?

MAYBE.

HEY, BUT AT LEAST YOU DON'T HAVE TO PAY FOR A NEW BODY—THE OLD ONE WAS GETTING A LITTLE SAGGY.

HAR HAR.

AH... NOW I REMEMBER.

WHAT?

THAT'S THE BODY THEY USED IN THOSE BOMBINGS LAST WEEK AT THE UN BASE ON LUNA. DIDN'T YOU SEE IT ON TV?

WHAT? NO! ARE YOU SERIOUS?

YEAH, MAN.

WHOA. ...

THAT'S FUCKED.

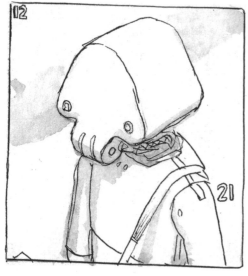

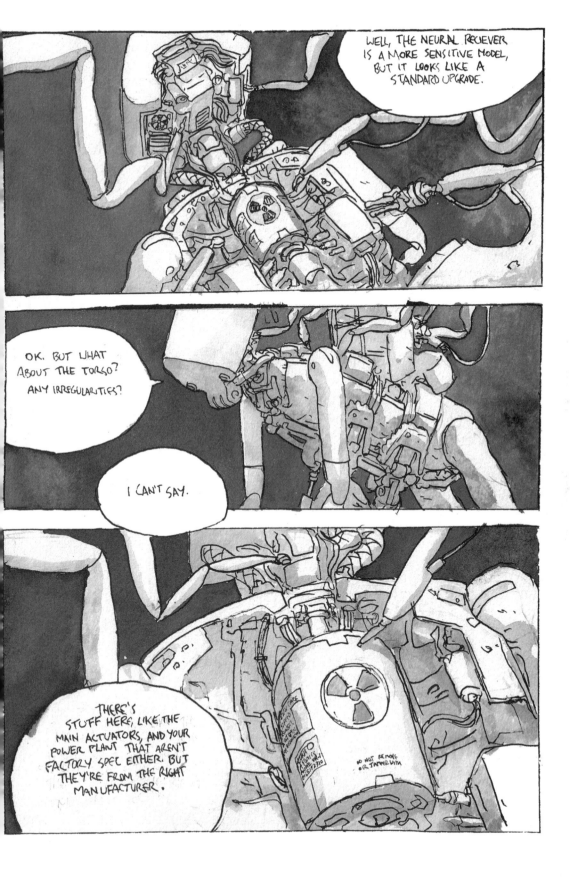

NOT WHAT I WANTED TO HEAR, DAVE.

I'M SORRY, BUT I JUST DON'T KNOW. ALL THE FILES ON CONSUMER GOODS FROM LUNA WERE LOCKED DURING THE WAR.

YOU'LL HAVE TO CHECK OUT THE DEALERSHIP THE BODY CAME FROM.

...FUCKING ANC INSURANCE...

YOU SHOULD REALLY SWITCH TO MY GUYS. IF YOU DID YOUR INSURANCE THROUGH GAZBANK—

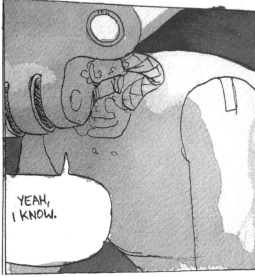

YEAH, I KNOW.

OKAY.
SO HANS HERE—

OFFICER DREIBURG.

SORRY, OFFICER DREIBURG HERE WAS JUST TALKING TO POLICE HEADQUARTERS.

SINCE YOUR BODY'S LUNAR-MADE, AND THE POSSIBILITY, UHH, OF YOU ACTUALLY BEING A BOMB IS LOOKING PRETTY GOOD, WE'RE UNDER ORDERS TO DELIVER YOU TO INTERPOL HQ.

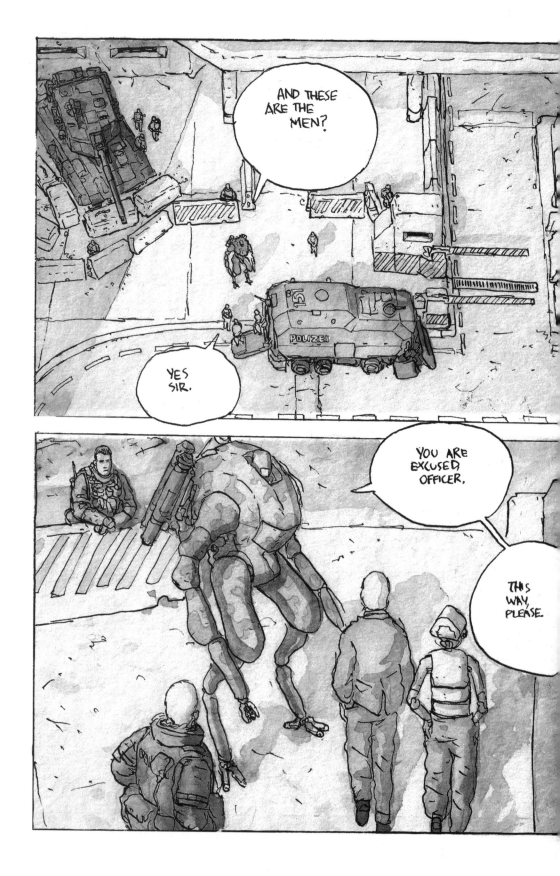

AFTERNOON, BOYS.

DING

TOMAS PRZEWORSKI, LT COMMANDER ANTI TERROR DEPT.

JAN NILSSEN.

AND I'M ANDERS STAUD.

TO BE HONEST, WE'VE BEEN WAITING FOR AN ATTACK ON EARTH SINCE BEFORE FRA MAURO.

THE EXAMINATION ROOM IS DOWN HERE.

AFTER WE KILLED RUSLAN SOSLAMBEKOV LAST FALL IN BRUSSELS, WE'VE KNOWN SOMETHING WAS COMING.

WE JUST DIDN'T KNOW THE BOMB WOULD FALL INTO OUR LAPS LIKE THIS.

I THINK JUST ELECTRO-MAGNETIC SHIELDING.

LIKE, A FARADAY CAGE?

YEAH.

HMM. AND HOW ABOUT RADIATION?

ONLY MINIMAL SHIELDING. PROBABLY JUST SOME LEAD IN THE WALLS.

GOOD.

WHAT ARE YOU—

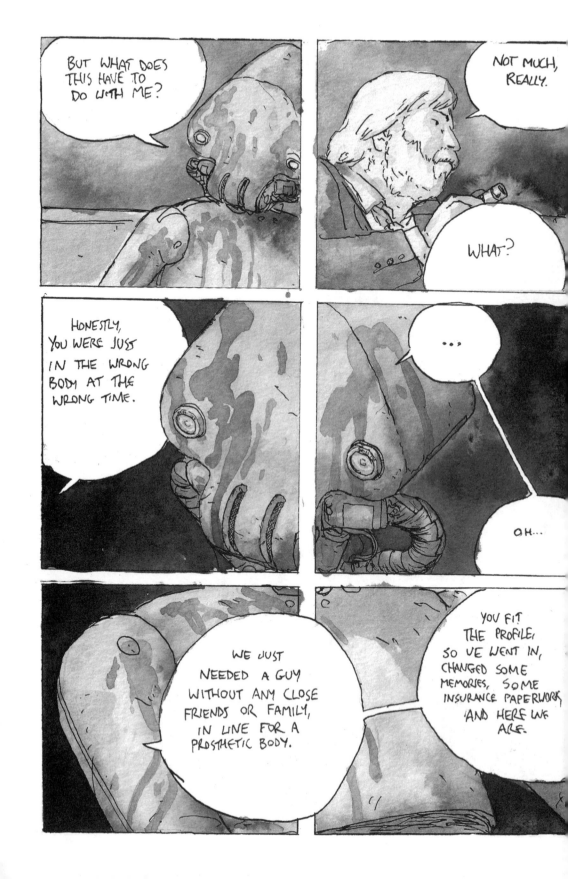

AH!
DONE!

RUNNING:
LITTLE DOCTOR
(APPLICATION 23 08)

-1:10⁵⁴

LOCKED

AND JAN, I KNOW THIS MAY NOT MEAN MUCH TO YOU RIGHT NOW, BUT I AM SORRY IT TURNED OUT THIS WAY.

YEAH.

ME TOO, MAN.

ME TOO.

SIMON ROY IS AN ARTIST AND
STUDENT, BORN IN 1988 IN
VICTORIA, BC, HE'S SPENT
MUCH OF HIS TIME SINCE
THEN COLLECTING AND READING
OLD SCI-FI PAPERBACKS, DRAWING,
AND PAINTING. CURRENTLY, HE
IS PURSUING A DEGREE IN
ILLUSTRATION AT THE ALBERTA
COLLEGE OF ART AND DESIGN.
THIS IS HIS FIRST BOOK.